Fireman Bill and Catch That Crab!

'Fireman Bill' and 'Catch That Crab!'
An original concept by Elizabeth Dale
© Elizabeth Dale

Illustrated by Serena Lombardo

Published by MAVERICK ARTS PUBLISHING LTD

Studio 11, City Business Centre, 6 Brighton Road,

Horsham, West Sussex, RH13 5BB

© Maverick Arts Publishing Limited February 2020

+44 (0)1403 256941

A CIP catalogue record for this book is available at the British Library.

ISBN 978-1-84886-653-9

Maverick
publishing

www.maverickbooks.co.uk

Red

This book is rated as: Red Band (Guided Reading)
This story is mostly decodable at Letters and Sounds Phase 3.
Up to eight non-decodable story words are included.

Fireman Bill and Catch That Crab!

By **Elizabeth Dale**

Illustrated by
Serena Lombardo

The Letter F

Trace the lower and upper case letter with a finger. Sound out the letter.

*Around,
down,
lift,
cross*

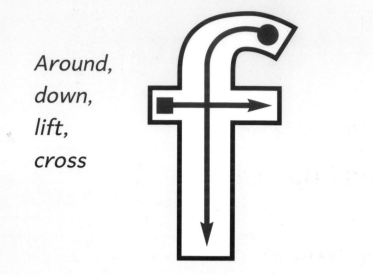

*Down,
lift,
cross,
lift,
cross*

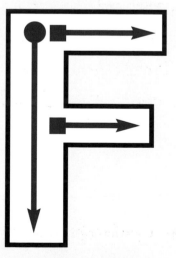

Some words to familiarise:

Bess   Jim   Meg

High-frequency words:

is   up   the   in   I

Tips for Reading 'Fireman Bill'

- Practise the words listed above before reading the story.

- If the reader struggles with any of the other words, ask them to look for sounds they know in the word. Encourage them to sound out the words and help them read the words if necessary.

- After reading the story, ask the reader why Fireman Bill needed rescuing.

Fun Activity

Discuss other things that firefighters do.

Fireman Bill

Kev is stuck up the tree.
Quick! Ring Fireman Bill.

Fireman Bill saves Kev. Hooray!

Liz is stuck in the well.

Quick! Ring Fireman Bill.

Fireman Bill saves Liz. Hooray!

Bess is stuck in the bog.
Quick! Ring Fireman Bill.

Fireman Bill saves Bess. Hooray!

Fireman Bill gets stuck in the bog!

Jim and Meg get stuck in the bog too!

Bess saves Fireman Bill,
Jim and Meg.

Hooray for Bess and Bill!

The Letter H

Trace the lower and upper case letter with a finger. Sound out the letter.

*Down,
up,
around,
down*

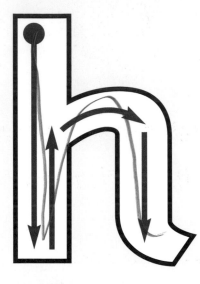

*Down,
lift
down,
lift,
cross*

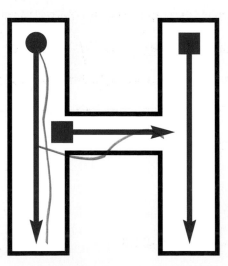

Some words to familiarise:

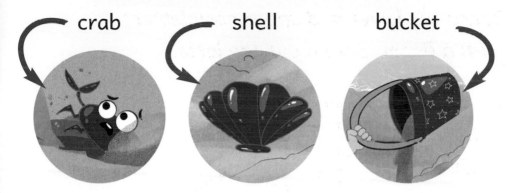

crab   shell   bucket

High-frequency words:

a she I it is the no we go his

Tips for Reading 'Catch That Crab!'

- Practise the words listed above before reading the story.

- If the reader struggles with any of the other words, ask them to look for sounds they know in the word. Encourage them to sound out the words and help them read the words if necessary.

- After reading the story, ask the reader how the crab got Dad's hat.

Fun Activity

Walk sideways like a crab!

Catch That Crab!

Jess spots a crab.

I must catch it!

She digs and digs.

Is this the crab?

No, but it is a big rock.

Jess digs and digs.

Is this the crab?

No, but it is a red shell.

Jess digs and digs.

Is this the crab?

No, but it is a fun bucket.

Dad looks for his hat.

He cannot spot it.

Look! Dad spots his hat...

...and the crab!

Book Bands for Guided Reading

The Institute of Education book banding system is a scale of colours that reflects the various levels of reading difficulty. The bands are assigned by taking into account the content, the language style, the layout and phonics. Word, phrase and sentence level work is also taken into consideration.

Maverick Early Readers are a bright, attractive range of books covering the pink to white bands. All of these books have been book banded for guided reading to the industry standard and edited by a leading educational consultant.

Pink

Red

Yellow

Blue

Green

Orange

Turquoise

Purple

Gold

White

To view the whole Maverick Readers scheme, visit our website at

www.maverickearlyreaders.com

Or scan the QR code above to view our scheme instantly!